More for Writing

Chris Buckton
Anne Sanderson

Series editor:
Leonie Bennett

Photocopy Masters
Differentiation and Homework

3

GINN

Author Team: Chris Buckton
Anne Sanderson
Series Editor: Leonie Bennett

Ginn

Linacre House, Jordan Hill, Oxford, OX2 8DP
a division of Reed Educational and Professional Publishing Ltd
www.ginn.co.uk

Ginn is a registered trademark of Reed Educational and Professional Publishing Ltd

ISBN 0602 296838

04 03 02 01 00
10 9 8 7 6 5 4 3 2 1

Designed by Gecko Ltd, Bicester, Oxon
Cover design by Gecko Ltd, Bicester, Oxon
Printed in the UK by Ashford Colour Press, Hampshire

Acknowledgements
The publisher would like to thank the following for permission to use their copyright
material:
PCM 9: from *Harry Moves House* by Chris Powling (A&C Black, 1993) reproduced by
permission of A&C Black (Publishers) Ltd; **PCM 23**: ending one from 'The Pudding Like a
Night on the Sea', from *The Julian Stories* © Ann Cameron, 1981 (Victor Gollancz/Hamish
Hamilton, 1983) reproduced by permission of Penguin Books Ltd; ending two from *The
Strongest Girl in the World* by Sally Gardner (Orion), reproduced by permission of the Orion
Publishing Group Ltd; **PCM 50**: from *Creatures of the Deep* by Lionel Bender © Aladdin
Books, 1989; **PCM 57**: from *Jake in Trouble* by Nick Butterworth (Hodder and Stoughton);
PCM 71: 'The Sound Collector' © Roger McGough, 1990, from *You Tell Me Poems* by
Roger McGough and Michael Rosen.

Contents

NAME _____ DATE _____

What makes me scared?

Who is in my family?

What is my favourite food?

ME

What do I like?

What do I wish?

Who is my best friend?

NAME _____ DATE _____

Characters

Setting

Events

Beginning: How will your story start?

↓

Middle: What will happen?

↓

Ending: How will it end?

NAME _____ DATE _____

Write a short description of where you live.

Cross out the words you don't need.

Where I live

I live in a city / town / village / in the middle of the country.

Three things I can see from my window are _____

_____

_____

_____

Three people I might see are _____

_____

_____

_____

Three sounds I might hear are _____

_____

_____

_____

NAME _____ DATE _____

Title _____

It was a _____ , _____ day in

the playground. _____ could see

_____

_____

There were lots of children _____

_____

_____

All around was the _____ sound of

_____

_____

Then suddenly _____

_____

_____

NAME _____ DATE _____

What am I saying?

1 Look at box 3.

This cat is:

☐ **angry**

☐ **happy**

☐ **asleep**

2 Why is the cat rubbing against the girl in box 4?

☐ **it is cold**

☐ **it wants to leave its smell on her**

3 **What cats want to say**	**How they tell you**
Hi there!	miaow loudly
	rub fur against you
I'm happy!	
Go away!	

NAME _____ DATE _____

Non-fiction books

Join each item in list 1 to the reason 'why it is useful' in list 2.

One line has been drawn for you.

1 What it is

2 Why it is useful

A dictionary   show you what things look like

The contents page   tells you what words mean

A heading   tells you what a section is about

A sub-heading   tells you on what pages you can find information

Diagrams and pictures   tells you what the page is about

An index   tells you what is in the book

NAME _____ DATE _____

Topic _____

Main heading:

Introduction:

Sub-heading:

Sub-heading:

Sub-heading:

Summary:

NAME _____ DATE _____

Look at the text below.

■ Some of the speech marks have been taken out. (" ")

■ There are **three** commas missing. (,)

■ There are **two** question marks missing. (?)

Add in the missing punctuation.

The children looked at each other in horror. " I didn't break it , " said Sam.

Neither did I ! said Katya.

" Well, someone must have broken it " said Mum. Which one of you was it

Just then the dog came bounding into the room. He jumped up at Mum.

Get down, Ben! shouted Mum.

That dog has too much energy said Dad. I've taken him for a walk and he's still not tired out.

" Did you hear anything smash when you left " asked Mum.

" Oh dear " said Dad. Has Ben broken something?

" Yes! " said the children together.

NAME _____ DATE _____

Put in the missing capital letters, speech marks (" ") and commas (,).

I don't think ... began Dad.

or a lighthouse! A working lighthouse! said Harry.

now look here ... said Dad.

how about a haunted grange then? Like the one I saw on Ghose Trail! said Harry.

harry ... said Dad

or a penthouse with a swimming pool! That would be smashing! shouted Harry.

very funny, Harry said Dad.

NAME _____ DATE _____

Ace Dragon Ltd

A play adapted from the story by Russell Hoban

Scene 1

John is walking down a street when he hears something go KLONK. He looks down and sees a round iron cover, with Ace Dragon Ltd written on it. He stamps on it and hears a voice from underground.

Ace:	Who is it?
John:	John.
Ace:	*(Grumpily)* What do you want?
John:	I want to know what Ltd means.
Ace:	It means limited.
John:	What does limited mean?
Ace:	It means I can't do everything. I can only do some things.
John:	What can you do?
Ace:	I can make fire come out of my nose and mouth. I can fly. I can spin gold into straw if you have any gold.
John:	I don't have any gold.
Ace:	Do you need any straw?
John:	No!
Ace:	Then it doesn't matter. Do you want to go flying with me?
John:	*(Excitedly)* Yes I do.
Ace:	Then you have to come down and fight me. If you win, I'll take you flying.

(John pulls the iron cover but it doesn't move)

John:	I can't lift this iron cover. It's too heavy. Can you lift it?
Ace:	Take the Underground to Dragonham East. I'll meet you there.

NAME _____ DATE _____

This is **Scene 2** of the play **Ace Dragon Ltd**.
But the writer has missed out:

     5 colons (:)

     3 question marks (?)

     2 exclamation marks (!)

Read the play on your own, or with another person. Think about how the lines should sound. Add in the missing punctuation.

Scene 2

John took the train to Dragonham East. There he saw a dragon.

Dragon: How do you do? I'm Ace Dragon Limited.

John   How do you do? I'm John.

Ace   Shall we do best of three fights

John: Right

(Ace and John have their first fight. John wins. Ace and John have their second fight. John wins.)

John   That's two in a row. That's the best out of three. Now you have to take me flying!

Ace   Come on then, up you get.

(Jake gets on Ace's back and they fly off high into the sky.)

John: Can you do stunts   Can you do sky-writing with fire

Ace   Yes I can, but I'm running out of petrol

NAME _____ DATE _____

Ace Dragon Ltd (continued)

Scene 3

John:

Ace:

John:

(He slices off some gold with his sword.)

John:

(_____

_____)

Ace:

John:

Ace:

John:

Ace Dragon Ltd (continued)

NAME _____ DATE _____

What do you know about Neil's grandad? Fill in the word web below.

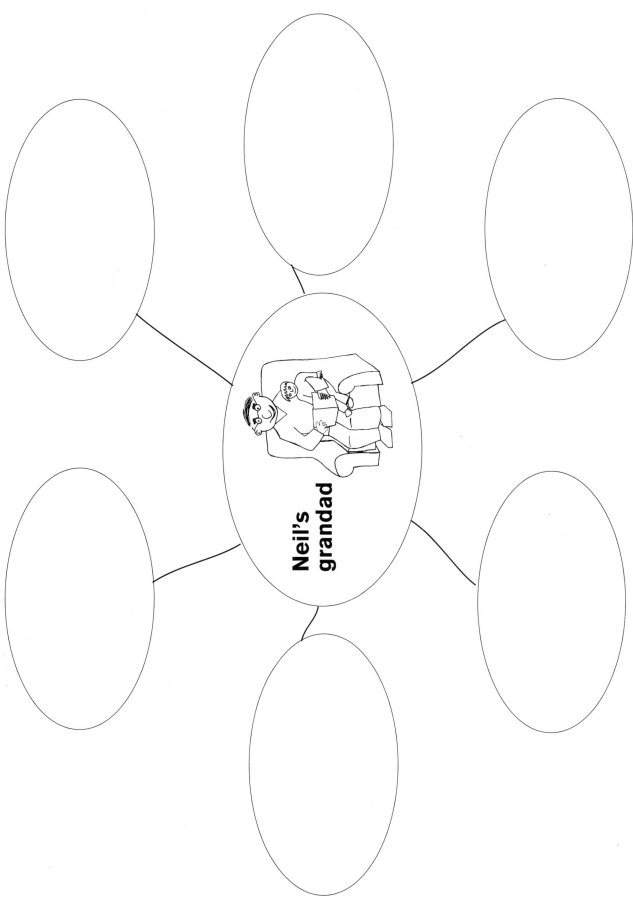

NAME _____ DATE _____

Flamborough

What can you do in Flamborough? What can you see? What can you hear?
Make notes under each heading.

Things to hear

Things to see

Things to do

NAME _____ DATE _____

1 Read the text below. Leslie wrote about somebody he knew in the past.

2 Change all the *verbs* from the past to the present tense. Make it sound as if Leslie knows the person now.

3 Read it again. Does it sound right?

A Really Nice Person

hear   am

When I <u>heard</u> the whistle of our milk man I <u>was</u> happy.

   comes

He <u>came</u> every morning to bring the milk and sometimes he <u>let</u> me

sit on his cart. He <u>was</u> always happy and <u>made</u> his customers

happy too.

I <u>liked</u> him because he <u>whistled</u> a happy tune. The milkman <u>came</u>

very early. Sometimes at five o'clock but I <u>didn't</u> care. He <u>wore</u> a

very white coat with blue writing on, as blue as the sky.

Leslie, age 8

NAME _____ DATE _____

Make up a word shape for each instrument.

recorder

triangle

guitar

violin

NAME _____ DATE _____

Look at the poem below. Change the words that are underlined into calligrams. Make them look like their meaning. One has been done for you.

HAUNTED HOUSE

The wind <u>moaned</u>

The door <u>creaked</u>

I heard footsteps <u>banging</u>

BANGING

There was blood on the stairs, <u>dripping</u>

I <u>screamed</u>

NAME _____ DATE _____

1 Look at the information about frogs in your book.

2 Label this Frog. Add some key facts to each label.

Tongue

long   sticky

NAME _____ DATE _____

1 Look at the Toad Fact Tree, then fill in this Fact Web about toads. One section has been done for you.

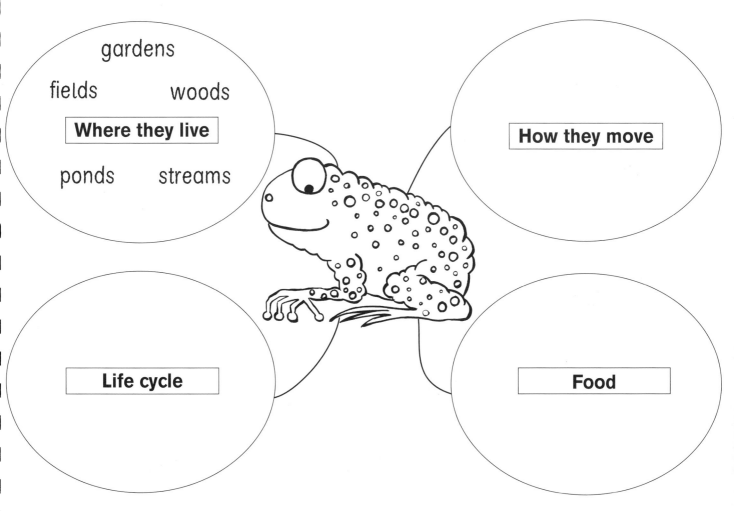

gardens

fields   woods

Where they live

ponds   streams

How they move

Life cycle

Food

2 Fill in the gaps in this report about toads.

Toads are amphibians. This means that they can live on land

and in _____ . The toad's skin is a _____

_____ colour. It is dry, rough and _____ .

Its head is short and _____ , and it has a short, fat body. A

toad cannot leap high. It mainly _____ or walks.

Toads eat spiders, insects and _____ .

NAME _____ DATE _____

Topic _____

subjects

A _____   B _____

characteristics

1 _____   1 _____

2 _____   2 _____

3 _____   3 _____

4 _____   4 _____

NAME _____ DATE _____

Title: _____

What I hate about _____

is _____

What I like about _____

is _____

What I hate about _____

is _____

and _____

_____

What I like about _____

is how _____

_____

NAME _____ DATE _____

Match these story endings to the openings in your book.

Ending 1

"A wonderful pudding," she said. "Would you like some, boys?"

"No thank you," we said.

She picked up a spoon. "Why this tastes like a whole raft of lemons," she said. "This tastes like a night on the sea."

Goes with opening:

Ending 2

As for Josie, she didn't mind that she was no longer the strongest little girl in the world.

She didn't miss her trick one bit. She was glad to be plain Josie Jenkins, now eight but soon to be nine years old.

Goes with opening:

Ending 3

Now the Lollipop Lady is quite recovered and is back at the school helping children across the road. And who do you think comes to meet her every afternoon at four o'clock?

Goes with opening:

NAME _____ DATE _____

Read this extract from The Lollipop Lady story.
There are 7 full stops and 6 capital letters missing.
Can you put them in the right places?

It was a quarter to four the Lollipop Lady stood in the middle of the road holding up her pole the pole was topped by a yellow circle like the sun STOP – CHILDREN was painted on it in black

It was raining the Lollipop Lady wore a white coat and black Wellingtons and a pink plastic headscarf every morning and every dinner-time and every afternoon she helped children to cross the road outside rylands primary School

NAME _____ DATE _____

Opening

_____ could do many tricks. He could _____

_____

He could _____

He could _____

He could _____

But the best trick _____

_____ . It was a trick that

changed his life.

It happened in the _____

when _____

_____

Ending

As for _____ , he didn't mind that he was no

longer the _____ boy in the world.

He didn't miss his trick one bit. He was glad to be plain _____

_____

_____

NAME _____ DATE _____

Look at the two story plans. What do they tell you? Fill in the chart below.

Vicky's plan

Jason's plan

Who is the story for?

What are the characters' names?

What are the characters like?

Where does the story happen?

What happens?

How does the story end?

HOMEWORK   UNIT 11 **Who? What? Where?** ● STORY PLANNING

PCM
27

NAME _____ DATE _____

How do you plan a story?

Tick the things you do. Write anything else in the boxes.

When I plan a story I

☐ do it in my head   ☐ use a story planner

☐ draw pictures   ☐ talk about it with someone

☐ make notes

> What else do you do?

I find it hard to plan

☐ the characters   ☐ the plot

☐ the beginning   ☐ the end

> What else do you find hard?

I find it easy to plan

☐ the characters   ☐ the plot

☐ the beginning   ☐ the end

> What else do you find easy?

SUPPORT   UNIT 11 **Who? What? Where?** • STORY PLANNING

PCM
28

NAME _____ DATE _____

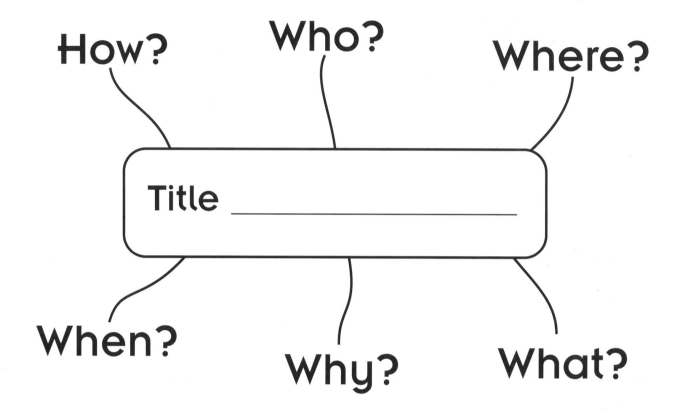

Beginning

Middle

End

NAME _____ DATE _____

Think of some adjectives to describe these characters. Write them on the character webs.

Goldilocks

Troll

Prince Charming

NAME _____ DATE _____

Write down the adjectives which mean the opposite of those below.

dark   <u>light</u>

kind   _____

angry   _____

smiling   _____

small   _____

loud   _____

thin   _____

young   _____

handsome   _____

polite   _____

NAME _____ DATE _____

WANTED

_____ **REWARD for the capture of:**

Name _____

Crime _____

Age _____ **Hair** _____

Eyes _____ **Nose** _____

Body _____

This person is very _____

_____

If you see this person please _____

_____

NAME _____ DATE _____

MISSING PERSON

_____ REWARD for the safe return of:

Name _____

Age _____ Hair _____

Eyes _____ Nose _____

Body _____

Habits _____

This person was last seen wearing _____

_____

This person likes _____

If you find this person please _____

_____

My Friend

Pete is the same age as me, that's 8, but his birthday is two weeks before mine.

He is very tall for his age, about 6cm taller than me, and he has got dark brown hair and brown eyes. He's good looking.

He's been my friend since we were at playschool. That's a long time ago, I think about 3 years. We went to the same playgroup just down the road.

He always lets me share his toys and games. He lets me use his brand new bike and sometimes when I go home with him I have goes on his Game Boy. If I get hurt or bullied he always helps me out. He's very kind.

NAME _____ DATE _____

name

looks

personality

family

interests

likes

dislikes

NAME _____ DATE _____

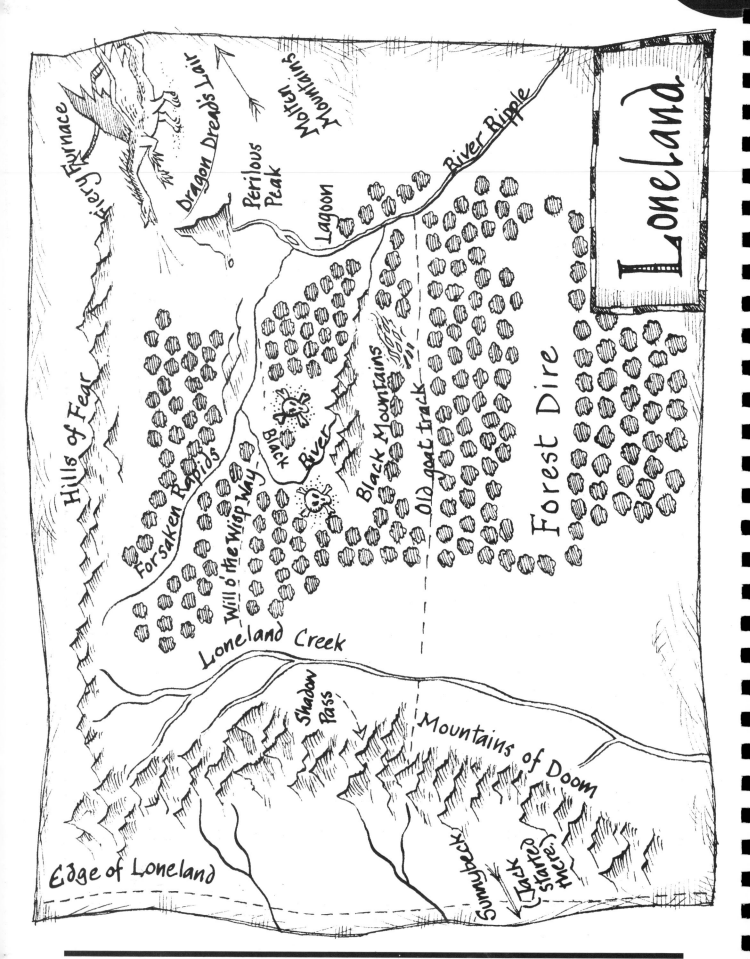

Loneland

Fiery Furnace

Dragon Dread's Lair

Molten Mountains

Perilous Peak

Lagoon

River Ripple

Hills of Fear

Forsaken Rapids

Black River

Will o' the Wisp Way

Black Mountains

Old Goat Track

Forest Dire

Loneland Creek

Shadow Pass

Mountains of Doom

Sunnybeck

(Jack started here)

Edge of Loneland

NAME _____ DATE _____

Look again at the yo-yo rules on pages 36–37.

---

1 Where might you find the Yo-yo rules?

in a book   on a yo-yo box   in a classroom

---

2 Three children roll a dice to start the Animal Safari game. Who goes first?

Sam rolls a 4   Eleanor rolls a 1   Meena rolls a 5

---

3 Join the beginning of each rule to its ending or reason.

RULE BEGINNING	RULE ENDING/REASON
Never look down over the yo-yo.	The highest score goes first.
Each player throws the dice.	Because it will make a mess.
Make sure your string is in good condition.	… you miss a turn.
If you land on 'Danger' …	Because it might hit you in the face.
Hamsters must not … leave food on the carpet.	Then it won't break.

---

4 Who might have written the rules? Complete these sentences.

The yo-yo rules could have been written by _____

_____

The Animal Safari rules could have been written by _____

_____

NAME _____ DATE _____

NAME _____ DATE _____

Too Much Searching – Story Chain

Start

Man

Rock

Antelope

Buffalo

Hunter

Vultures

People

Lesson _____

NAME _____ DATE _____

Look at the singular and plural nouns.

Can you find any more to fit the patterns?

Can you work out any rules?

Singular	Plural	Other plurals I have found
bush	bushes	_____ shes
cat	cats	_____ ts
day	days	_____ ys
tree	trees	_____ ees
princess	princesses	_____ sses
berry	berries	_____ ries
lady	ladies	_____ dies
bus	buses	_____ ses

NAME _____ DATE _____

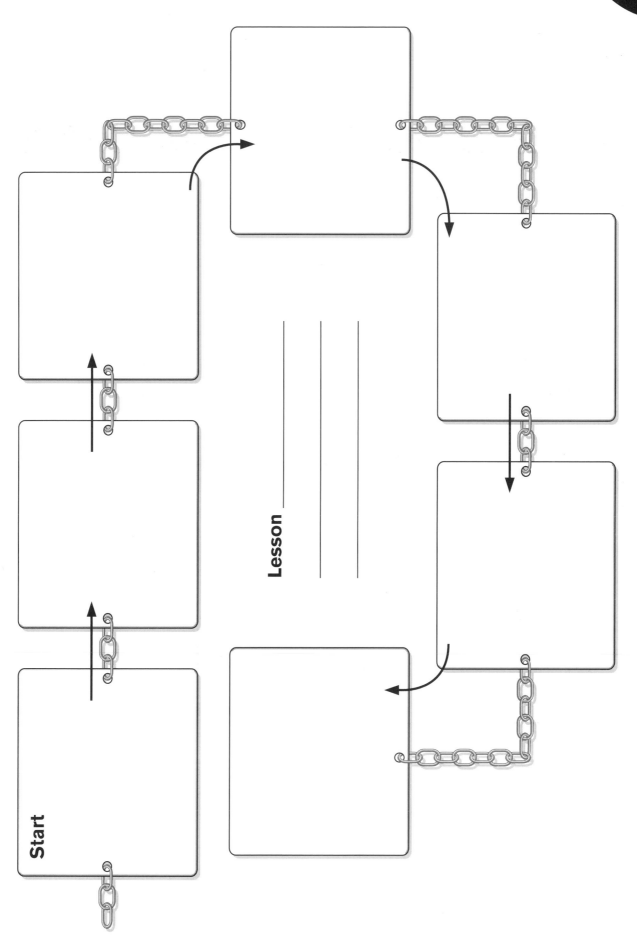

Lesson _____

Start

NAME _____ DATE _____

Read the story of Mighty Mountain. What typical ingredients of a traditional tale does it include? Make notes.

Opening?

Setting?

Characters?

Opposites?

Events?

Magic Objects?

Numbers?

Ending?

NAME _____ DATE _____

1 Look at the two sets of instructions in your books.

What is each one for? Who will read it?

Recipe

Recycled paper

2 Look at the Cookies recipe.

a) How much sugar do you need?

_____

b) How do you make a criss-cross pattern on the cookie dough?

_____

c) When are the cookies ready to eat? Underline the right answer.

when flattened   *when golden brown*   *when cool*

3 Read the instructions for recycling paper.

a) Why do you have to leave the mixture for a week?

_____

b) Why do you have to use a pair of tights to make the sieve?

_____

NAME _____ DATE _____

Instructions for an alien:
How to clean your teeth

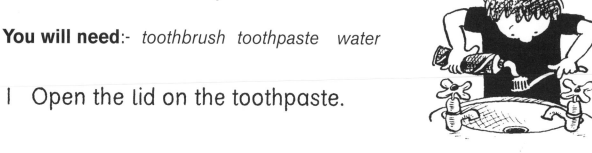

You will need:- *toothbrush toothpaste   water*

1 Open the lid on the toothpaste.

2 Squeeze _____

3 Turn on tap and _____

_____

4 _____

5 _____

6 _____

7 _____

8 _____

9 _____

10 _____

NAME _____ DATE _____

How to _____

You will need

What to do

1

2

3

4

5

6

NAME _____ DATE _____

1 Re-write the message to Daisy in complete sentences.

2 Complete each sentence. Underline the best word.

1 Daisy's message was (*a request   an invitation   a list*).

2 Benjie's list was a (*letter   reminder   telephone message*).

3 Mum's note to C was to (*remind   inform   ask*) him.

3 Write one or two sentences which explain what the headline is about.

Shark Spotted off Cornish Coast

NAME _____ DATE _____

Re-write each of these sentences as a short message. Take out the words that are not essential to meaning. The first one has been done for you.

I am having a great time on holiday.

Having a great time.

Sanjay rang you at 3.30 to say that the football match tonight has been cancelled.

_____

Remember to take your swimming costume to school tomorrow.

_____

We are having a disco at school on the last day of term.

_____

I got up late this morning and missed the school bus.

_____

NAME _____ DATE _____

My picture of the creature

I think it lost its toe when _____

_____

_____

NAME _____ DATE _____

The woman _____ even further down

under the covers and _____

Then Something _____

began to _____

Its eyes _____

Its hands _____

Its feet _____

The woman _____

_____

At last, _____

_____

In a _____ voice Something said: " _____

_____ "

Pronouns

1 Put a line under the *pronouns* in this paragraph. Two have been done for you.

Marcus was feeling bored and fed up. All <u>his</u> friends were on holiday, and his cousin Lila was coming to stay. <u>She</u> was a year older than Marcus and could be very bossy. He thought about Lila's last visit, when she made him climb the big old oak tree and helped her to build that stupid tree house. Marcus still had a scar on his left leg, where he caught it on a branch as he fell.

2 Add the missing pronouns.

Lila arrived on time, as usual. <u>She</u> had a great big smile on her face, as _____ came running towards Marcus.

'Hi Marcus,' _____ cried. 'I've got a great idea for a den.'

Marcus pretended not to hear. _____ turned up the sound on _____ computer game, and hoped that Lila would leave _____ alone.

But, no such luck!

_____ plonked down next to _____ and waited for him to switch _____ off.

NAME _____ DATE _____

Using apostrophes to shorten words

1 Read these sentences.

Re-write them with the shortened words in full.

There's a strange smell at the school.

_____

The parents aren't happy about it.

_____

2 Read these sentences and use apostrophes(') to shorten words.

I am holding a meeting at my house.

_____

It is now two weeks since the school closed.

_____

We will be asking the council what they plan to do

next.

_____

NAME _____ DATE _____

your address

_____

_____

_____

_____

_____

date

Dear

Yours

NAME _____ DATE _____

HEADLINE

BY

PARAGRAPH 1 (Introduce the event)	PICTURE

PARAGRAPH 2 (Describe the event)	PARAGRAPH 3 (Quotes)

NAME _____ DATE _____

Tuffy the Killer Cat

Once there was a killer cat called _____

He lived with _____and her mother and

_____ Tuffy liked killing _____

_____

One day, _____

He put the bird on the _____

Ellie was _____

She _____

Her mother and father were _____

Tuffy was _____

NAME _____ DATE _____

1 Read the story below.

Change some of the <u>nouns</u> into pronouns – he, she or it.

Tuffy was a cat. <u>Tuffy</u> killed a bird and then <u>Tuffy</u>

dragged <u>the bird</u> on to the carpet. Ellie was upset

because <u>Ellie</u> liked the bird and <u>Ellie</u> didn't want Tuffy

to hurt <u>the bird</u>. But <u>Tuffy</u> couldn't help killing birds

because <u>Tuffy</u> was a cat.

2 Find some more nouns. What happens if you change them into pronouns?
Does it still make sense?

NAME _____ DATE _____

Jake in Trouble

Jake was excited. He was going on holiday to a farm.

Jake had never been on holiday before and he had never been to a farm. He was looking forward to meeting all the animals. He knew there were sheep on the farm because he'd heard his owners, Mr and Mrs Foster, telling Sam.

Sam was Jake's favourite person. He lived in the house at the bottom of Jake's garden. Sam took Jake for walks in their local park. He always had a friendly word and pat for Jake.

Of course, Jake would miss his friends from the park, especially Holly, the collie, who lived next door. Jake told her how excited he was. He was especially looking forward to herding some sheep.

Holly didn't think he'd be allowed to do that. Farmers were very funny about their sheep. They were fussy about dogs. She'd even heard of a dog being shot at because he was in a field with sheep.

Jake found that hard to believe and thought that Holly was just being silly. He was sure he'd be able to do it. Jake reminded Holly that his grandfather was a Belgian Shepherd dog, so he had sheep herding in his blood.

Extract from *Jake in Trouble*
by Nick Butterworth

NAME _____ DATE _____

Diary of a happy dog

<u>Friday</u>

I'm so excited today because

I've never been to a   before.

I hope I'll see some

I want to

I'll really miss

NAME _____ DATE _____

Read the book reviews in your book.

Look at each of the features below. Does the writer include them in their review?

If they do, put ✔

If they do not, put ✗

If it's not clear put ?

	Narina	Tom
Title		
Author		
Genre		
What it's about		
Where it's set		
Who's in it		
Best or worst things		
Who might enjoy it		

NAME _____ DATE _____

Choose a book you have read recently. It can be fiction or non-fiction. Fill in the details below. Circle the words which describe your book. Add any other comments. Give it a star rating ★ = poor, ★ ★ ★ ★ ★ = fantastic!

Title _____

Author _____

Illustrator _____

This is a	story	poetry book	information book
I chose it because of	the title	the author	the cover
	it looked easy to read	I'd heard about it	I'd seen it on TV
It is	interesting	boring	exciting
	funny	helpful	sad
	too hard	too easy	just right for me

Any other comments _____

_____

_____

Star rating

NAME _____ DATE _____

Fiction Review

Title _____

Author _____

Genre _____

Where it's set

Who's in it

What it's about

Best or worst things

I would recommend this book to

NAME _____ DATE _____

Non-Fiction Review

Title _____

Author _____

Genre _____

What it's about

Illustrations

What I found out

Best or worst things

I would recommend this book to

NAME _____ DATE _____

Read the letter below.

1 Who do you think Mr Mayer might be?

2 What is the purpose of Chris's letter?

3 Is this a formal or informal letter? Underline the words that tell you.

---

14 Anfield Road
Bournemouth
BH40 3PA

14 May 2000

Dear Mr Mayer

I am writing to apologise for breaking the glass in your greenhouse.

When I kicked the ball to my friend, I didn't know it was going to bounce off the wall and over into your garden. It was an accident, and I'm very sorry that your greenhouse got broken. I hope the plants weren't too badly damaged.

My dad says he will pay for any damage, so please let me know what it costs to mend the greenhouse.

Yours sincerely

Chris Johnson

NAME _____ DATE _____

address

_____

Dear _____ ,   date

    I am writing to you because _____

_____

    I think your books/poems are _____

My favourite books/poems are _____

_____

_____

The bit I like best in _____

is where _____

    I would like to ask you some questions. First of all, _____

_____

Another question I would like to ask is _____

_____ .

    I do hope you will be able to reply to my letter.

    Yours sincerely

NAME _____ DATE _____

BEGINNING – set the scene

Chapter 1 Marooned!

Who? Jamie, Steve, Sam

Where? at their school

What? water burst from roadworks, floods, boys are trapped in school

---

MIDDLE – what happens next?

Chapter 2 The Worst Lunch Ever

school dinners can't get through the flood

water is rising outside

they notice water coming in through the door, everyone is scared

---

MIDDLE – things get worse

Chapter 3 Night Time Frights

MIDDLE – climax/big event

Chapter 4 Disaster!

ENDING – everything is sorted out

Chapter 5 Rescued at Last

NAME _____ DATE _____

TRAPPED!

Brainstorm ideas for a story about being trapped in school.

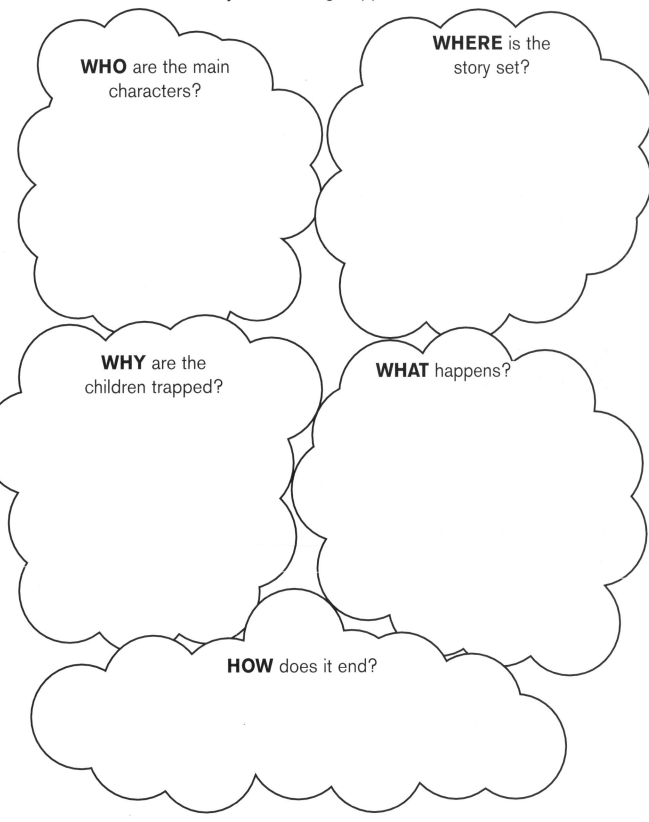

WHO are the main characters?

WHERE is the story set?

WHY are the children trapped?

WHAT happens?

HOW does it end?

NAME _____ DATE _____

TRAPPED!

BEGINNING – set the scene
Chapter 1 Marooned!

MIDDLE – what happens next?
Chapter 2 The Worst Lunch Ever

MIDDLE – things get worse
Chapter 3 Night Time Frights

MIDDLE – climax/big event
Chapter 4 Disaster!

ENDING – everything is sorted out
Chapter 5 Rescued at Last

NAME _____ DATE _____

Chapter 2
The Worst Lunch Ever

It was quarter past twelve, lunchtime! Sam sat down and waited for his hot lunch. He waited for five minutes until the head came in and said: "I'm sorry children, there are no hot dinners today because the dinner couldn't arrive through the flood."

Everyone sighed, but mostly Sam. "I wonder what we're going to eat," Sam wondered. He went to Jamie and Steve and sighed. "Can you believe it. No hot lunches!"

Meanwhile the water was still rising.

Suddenly there was a shout.

"Come quick!" It was Charlotte.

The three of them rushed to the door, but they had to wait ten minutes before it was their turn to go and look at the water. It was rising fast. Steve, Jamie and Sam stood at the door staring at the glittering, giant puddle of dirty water. Suddenly the water crept through a crack in the door. A shiver ran down their spines. They were frightened.

Jakk and Ranjit, age 8

NAME _____ DATE _____

All the paragraphs and speech punctuation have been removed from the story.
Add in the speech marks and other speech punctuation.

Put a line in the text where a new paragraph is needed. One has been done
for you.

Chapter 1 Marooned!

There had been waterworks on Earlham Road for over a
month now! / It took the children a long time to get home.
Steve, Jamie and Sam were sick of it. I wonder how long
this will go on for wondered Sam. Jamie and Steve
wondered too. It's probably going to take five weeks said
Sam. The next day the three boys walked to school
together. Suddenly they heard a shout from near the
roadworks: HELP They saw water pouring out from the
roadworks. So they ran for their lives all the way to school.
They burst through the classroom doors shouting FLOOD!
Then shut the door! ordered Charlotte, and so they did. The
head walked in and said I'm sorry children, we are
marooned for a month.

NAME _____ DATE _____

TRAPPED!

Draft one of your chapters using the framework below.

Think about what each paragraph will do. You could include some dialogue.

CHAPTER _____

> **Paragraph 1 – Set the scene. What is the atmosphere like?**

> **Paragraph 2 – How do your characters feel? What do they say?**

> **Paragraph 3 – Introduce action and drama**

> **Paragraph 4 – Build up the tension**

> **Paragraph 5 – End on a cliffhanger**

NAME _____ DATE _____

The Sound Collector

A stranger called this morning
Dressed all in black and grey
Put every sound into a bag
And carried them away.

The whistling of the kettle
The turning of the lock
The purring of the kitten
The ticking of the clock

The popping of the toaster
The crunching of the flakes
When you spread the marmalade
The scraping noise it makes

The hissing of the frying pan
The ticking of the grill
The bubbling of the bathtub
As it starts to fill

The drumming of the raindrops
On the window-pane
When you do the washing-up
The gurgle of the drain

The crying of the baby
The squeaking of the chair
The swishing of the curtain
The creaking of the stair

A stranger called this morning
He didn't leave his name
Left us only silence
Life will never be the same.

Roger McGough.

NAME _____ DATE _____

Afternoon Sound Collector

1 What do you hear as you leave the classroom, and go home?

2 List what you hear in the first column.

3 Think of a word to imitate the sound. Write it in the second column.

   You might need to invent spellings for some sound words.

What I heard	The sound it made
book bag dropping on the floor	splat

NAME _____ DATE _____

Afternoon

Afternoon

Afternoon ends

    with _____

Afternoon ends

    with _____

Afternoon ends

    with _____

Afternoon ends

    with _____

Afternoon ends

    with _____

Afternoon ends

    with _____

Afternoon ends

    with me just listening

Afternoon ends and takes me home from school

_____ afternoon.

NAME _____ DATE _____

How life was in a North American Indian camp

The Indians lived in tipis. The tipis were made from buffalo skin or moose skin. Inside the tipis there were two or three poles going up the middle. Some of the Indians lived in earth lodges. Earth lodges were made of grass and mud. The mud sticks all the grass together. Some of the Indians lived in wigwams. A wigwam is a birch bark that the Indians built.

Tribes who settled in one place grew lots of crops such as pumpkins and artichokes. Most important was corn and maize. Corn was one of the main sources of food. To some tribes it was important for their ceremonies.

In America there are lots of animals such as buffalo, deer, elk, horses and dogs. Animals are important to the American Indians. Dogs were used for hunting, and to pull sledges around. Horses were used for riding. Elk, deer and buffalo skins were used for making clothes. Buffalos had thick furry coats and Indians used their skins to make coats and blankets. The Indians wore a kind of shoe called moccasins. The girls wore dresses made from deer skins.

The men went hunting and fishing, while the women gathered fruit and vegetables. Some men made canoes.

Some tribes like the Dakota, Blackfeet and Crow, do a dance called the sun dance. The Indians did sports as well, including horse racing, archery and ball games. Some tribes played a game called 'Lacrosse' using sticks with baskets.

Some Indians wore feathers. They did this to show how important they were.

JADE, age 10

NAME _____ DATE _____

don't know

disagree

agree

1 Stories are easy to write.

2 Writing is the most important thing we do in school.

3 It's important to write neatly.

4 Silence is best for writing.

5 You have to be clever to write well.

6 Teachers should correct all mistakes.

7 Starting a piece of writing is the hardest thing.

8 The longer the writing, the better it is.

9 Talking to a friend helps you write.

10 The best stories have happy endings.

11 Bad spelling spoils good writing.

NAME _____ DATE _____

What makes a good writer?

> **What does a good writer do?**

> **How does someone become a good writer?**

> **What different kinds of writing do you do?**

> **What writing have you done that you are really proud of?**

> **What do you find hard?**

> **What do you find easy?**

NAME _____ DATE _____

The kind of writing I have done most of is _____

The kind of writing I have done least of is _____

I think I have got better at _____

_____

My new targets are _____

_____

PROMPT CHART 1

Story Writing

Setting

Use small details to build up a picture –
What can you see?
What can you hear?
What can you smell?

☆

Give clues to what the story is about.

☆

Make the reader want to know more.

Character

What do they look like?

☆

What kind of person are they?

☆

What do they do?

☆

What do they say?

Main Events

How will the story start?

☆

What problems will there be?

☆

How will the problems be sorted out?

☆

How will your story end?

PROMPT CHART 2

Report

Introduce the subject.

Use the present tense.

Try to keep to the facts.

Not too many opinions.

Playscripts

Stage Directions

Set the scene.

Tell the actors how to say their lines.

Tell the actors what to do.

Use brackets.

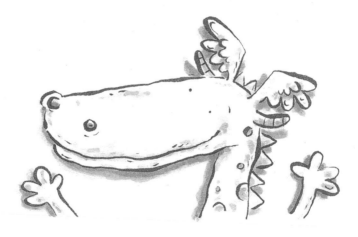

Layout

Use a colon after the name.

Don't use speech marks.

Don't use 'said'.

e.g. (*Jack runs into the kitchen.*)

Jack: Look, Mum!

PROMPT CHART 4

Story Openings and Endings

Story Openings

Set the scene.

◆

Introduce the main characters.

◆

Make the reader interested.

◆

Plant clues to what the story is about.

Grab the reader with:

surprising dialogue

◆

a mystery

◆

a description that makes them want to read more

Story Endings

Plant clues before you get there.

◆

Tie up loose ends

◆

Don't end it too quickly.

Rules and Instructions

INSTRUCTIONS

Tell the reader what they will need.

▍

Make the instructions clear and easy to follow.
Use:
clear layout to fit the purpose
easy to follow steps
logical order
dashes, bullet points, numbers etc.

▍

Put the verb at the beginning of the sentence.

RULES

Use short clear sentences.

▍

Put the verb at the beginning of the sentence.

PROMPT CHART 6

The Ingredients of a Traditional Tale

Openings:	'Once upon a time . . .' 'Long, long ago . . .' 'There once was . . .'
	¥
Settings:	forest, castle, strange land, poor cottage
	¥
Characters:	prince, princess, poor woodcutter, farmer, villager, witch, giant, monster
	¥
Opposites:	good and bad wise and foolish weak and strong
	¥
Events:	journeys, quests, trials, forfeits, amazing feats
	¥
Magic objects:	rings, wands, keys
	¥
Numbers:	3 bears, 3 wishes, 3 sisters
	¥
Endings:	'From that day on . . .' '. . . happily ever after' '. . . never went there again'

OHT Correlation Chart

In recognition of the fact that not all schools are equipped with the facilities for using overhead transparencies, we have supplied here as additional photocopiable sheets, any OHTs which do not appear elsewhere, either as text in the Pupil's Book or PCMs.

Below is a correlation chart, which will help you to match the OHT reference in the Teacher's Book to the appropriate Pupil's Book extract, PCM or additional photocopiable sheet.

UNIT	OHT reference from Teacher's Book	Cross reference to appropriate PCM, Pupil's Book page or additional photocopiable sheet
1	OHT 1	Provided here as a photocopiable sheet
1	OHT 2	PCM 2
2	OHT 3	Use flipchart with headings Sights Sounds Smells
3	OHT 4	PCM 7
4	OHT 5	Pupil's Book pages 10–11
4	OHT 6	Provided here as a photocopiable sheet
5	OHT 7	Pupil's Book page 12
5	OHT 8	Provided here as a photocopiable sheet
6	OHT 9	Provided here as a photocopiable sheet
7	OHT 10	Provided here as a photocopiable sheet
8	OHT 11	PCM 21
9	OHT 12	Provided here as a photocopiable sheet
10	OHT 13	Pupil's Book pages 24–25
10	OHT 14	PCM 25
11	OHT 15	PCM 28
12	OHT 16	Pupil's Book pages 30–31
12	OHT 17	PCM 31
13	OHT 18	Pupil's Book page 32
13	OHT 19	PCM 34
14	OHT 20	Pupil's Book page 34 (map)
15	OHT 21	PCM 37
16	OHT 22	Provided here as a photocopiable sheet
17	OHT 23	Provided here as a photocopiable sheet
18	OHT 24	PCM 44
20	OHT 25	PCM 48
21	OHT 26	Pupil's Book page 51
21	OHT 27	PCM 50
22	OHT 28	PCM 53
22	OHT 29	PCM 54
23	OHT 30	PCM 57
24	OHT 31	PCM 61
24	OHT 32	PCM 62
25	OHT 33	PCM 64
26	OHT 34	PCM 67
27	OHT 35	PCM 70
28	OHT 36	PCM 71
28	OHT 37	PCM 73
29	OHT 38	PCM 74
29	OHT 39	Provided here as a photocopiable sheet
30	OHT 40	PCM 77

Who is my favourite person?

What makes me scared?

Who is in my family?

What is my favourite food?

What do I hate?

Worst food?

What do I like?

ME

What is my bedroom like?

What is my favourite colour?

Who listens to me?

What do I want to be when I grow up?

What are my favourite clothes?

What would I do if I won £1 000 000?

Harry Moves House *Chris Powling*

I also knew that Mum had made up her mind about moving so it
was no use arguing. Especially as Dad seemed to agree with her.

'Cheer up, Harry,' he said. 'The new house will be smashing, I
promise. And you can help us choose it if you like.'

Title _____

Scene

_____ : _____

_____ : _____

_____ _____

_____ _____

_____ _____

_____ _____

_____ _____

_____ _____

(_____)

Title of report _____

Introduction

Paragraph 2 _____

Paragraph 3 _____

Paragraph 4 _____

Summary

Holiday Memories

It was FREEZING cold

and I was feeling really *Fed up*

and **SOAKED** to the skin!

I remembered the *Fantastic*

holiday in Spain –

 ROASTING hot weather, clear blue sea,

 BOILING beaches and a clear sky.

Now it's all a memory.

Paula Edwards

Subject _____

☹ HATE	LIKE ☺

What I hate about _____

is _____

What I like about _____

is _____

chaos

climax

Start

lesson

Mighty Mountain continued ...

Opening

What happens?

What does Mighty Mountain do?

What do the three women do?

Magic objects/Numbers?

New setting?

New characters?

Ending

An A to Z of

A

B

C

D